Harriet and the Runaway Book

Johanna Johnston

Harriet and the Runaway Book

The Story of
Harriet Beecher Stowe
and UNCLE TOM'S CABIN

Illustrations by Ronald Himler

Harper & Row, Publishers
New York, Hagerstown
San Francisco, London

Harriet and the Runaway Book
Text copyright © 1977 by Johanna Johnston
Illustrations copyright © 1977 by Ronald Himler

Library of Congress Cataloging in Publication Data
Johnston, Johanna.
    Harriet and the runaway book.

    SUMMARY: A biography of the woman who wrote
Uncle Tom's Cabin, stressing the experiences and
impressions which caused her to write the famous
book denouncing slavery.
    1. Stowe, Harriet Elizabeth Beecher, 1811-1896
—Juvenile literature. 2. Authors, American—
19th century—Biography—Juvenile literature.
3. Slavery in the United States—Juvenile literature.
[1. Stowe, Harriet Elizabeth Beecher,
1811-1896. 2. Authors, American. 3. Slavery
in the United States] I. Himler, Ronald.
II. Title.
PS2956.J59   1977   818'.3'09   [B]   [92]   76—24305
ISBN 0-06-022839-3
ISBN 0-06-022840-7 lib. bdg.

Designed by Kohar Alexanian

Harriet and the Runaway Book

1

Every so often she ran away.
"Hattie," they called. "Hattie!"
And then, "Harriet!"
But she didn't answer,
although she had never gone far.

Sometimes she was in the same room.
But her blue-gray eyes were half-closed.
She wasn't seeing or hearing anything around her.
She was off in a dream world of her own.

Her brothers and sisters shrugged and laughed.
"Oh, never mind," they said.
"Hattie's owling around again.
She'll come to when she's ready."
And, of course, she always did come to,
ready to set her small brother Henry Ward to laughing
by making monkey faces—
ready to run out to the garden
to help her sisters, Catherine and Mary, pick beans—
ready to join in whatever was going on.

9

And with eight children in the big Beecher house,
and a father like Lyman Beecher,
there usually was something going on.

"All right, everybody," Lyman Beecher called.
"All hands out back
for the great woodcutting and stacking contest."
Hattie was there in a flash, her brown curls flying.
Her big brothers, William, Edward, and George,
swung the axes and split the logs.
Then Hattie carried an armload of wood
to the woodshed, stacked it, and ran back
for another load.
"Look at Hattie!" Lyman Beecher called to the boys.
"She's doing more than any of you!"
Hattie ran even faster with the loads of wood
until the job was finished.

"Well done!" said Lyman Beecher.
"Now all hands can celebrate by going fishing
on Long Pond."
At supper, Lyman Beecher
sharpened his children's wits
by starting family debates.

"Tell me," he said one night,
pushing his spectacles up on his forehead
and looking around the table,
"what is mankind's most useful invention?"

William, the oldest boy, blinked and frowned.
"Well, sir, people generally say the wheel."
Edward, the next oldest, spoke up.
"How about moveable type, Pa?
After that was invented, books could be printed cheaply
and everyone could own a Bible."
George, who liked jokes and music, chimed in next.
"How about the man who strung the first harp?
Without his harp, would King David
have sung his psalms?"

Lyman Beecher laughed.
"You all have points.
Now let's hear your arguments."
But Hattie was waving her hand.
"Please, Pa," she said eagerly,
"how about the lever?"
"Aha!" cried her father.
"Let's hear more, Hattie."

Her eyes shining, Hattie rushed on.
"When man invented the lever,
he was able to move things
he could never move before.
With the lever, he could use a little effort
and move a—a mountain."
"Excellent, Hattie, excellent," said her father.
He looked around the table and shook his head.
"If only she'd been a boy."

Hattie tried not to feel hurt when her father said that.
She knew what he meant.
Lyman Beecher was a minister.
Sundays, he stood in the white meeting house
in Litchfield, Connecticut,
and preached such wonderful sermons
that he was famous through all New England.
He was sure that ministers, who helped save souls,
did the most important work in the world.

He wanted all his sons to be ministers,
but of course he could not have such a dream
for a daughter.
Only boys could grow up to be ministers
or doctors or lawyers, or anything like that.
About all a girl could be when she grew up
was a wife and mother.

Hattie knew that. Everybody did.
So she understood her father meant to praise her
when he wished she were a boy.
And she kept on trying to be as quick and clever
as her brothers.

And she kept on running away sometimes too,
owling around with her eyes half-closed.
Nobody worried.
It was just Hattie's way.

2

Along with her older sister Mary,
Hattie went to Miss Pierce's Academy,
just down the road from the Beecher house.
She was small for her age, and shy away from home,
so nobody noticed her much as she went
from one class to another,
studying Latin and French and geography,
art and music and English composition.
Sometimes her drawing teacher praised her pictures
of flowers or fruit.

Her English teacher, Mr. Brace,
gave her good marks on her themes.

The best part of the day came for Hattie
when she was home again,
curled up by a little window in the attic
with a book.
The attic had a comfortable smell
from the apples and onions and herbs stored there.
And among her father's books,
Hattie had found a few that were magical.
Curled up in her corner,
she followed the adventures of Sinbad,
in *The Arabian Nights,*
or Christian, in *Pilgrim's Progress,*
or Ivanhoe, in Sir Walter Scott's novel.

"Hattie!"
The call from downstairs always came too soon.
But there were chores to be done—
cooking, baking, churning,
washing, ironing, sewing—
and Hattie had to help.

She dreamed through some of the boring chores,
and sometimes her stepmother spoke sharply.
"Hattie! Pay attention!
You'll never learn to make buttonholes that way."
Sometimes Hattie felt she couldn't do anything right.

Then, one bright day in June,
Miss Pierce's Academy held graduating exercises.
The most important people in town
were on the platform to watch.
Lyman Beecher was there, of course.
One by one, the teachers read aloud
their pupils' prize compositions.

Suddenly, Hattie's teacher, Mr. Brace,
was reading words that Hattie knew very well.
She hardly knew where to look.
When he finished, there was a lot of clapping.
Hattie saw her father clapping harder than anyone.
She saw him whisper to Mr. Brace.
Then Mr. Brace pointed at *her*.
After the exercises, her father kissed her
and spoke proudly to all his friends.

"Just think, she's only thirteen."
Then he shook his head.
"She should have been a boy."

This time Hattie didn't mind.
There *was* something she could do
even if she was a girl.
She could *write*
so that people paid attention.

That was the start of a happy summer.
Hattie rambled in the meadows with Henry Ward.
She went on family picnics and fishing expeditions.
Sometimes she wrote little stories or poems.
She even got a little better
at making buttonholes.

3

"Can any of us guess what it means to be a slave?"
Lyman Beecher stood high in the pulpit
and looked down at the congregation.
"Try to imagine *yourself*
kidnapped from your homeland,
chained to a dozen others, crowded into a filthy ship,
half-dying through the storms of a long voyage...

then being unloaded and sold
like a horse, a cow, or a pig."
His voice rose. "Can you *feel* what it is like?"

Down in the Beecher pew, Hattie closed her eyes
and imagined being kidnapped,
imagined iron bracelets on her wrists,
iron chains clanking from her ankles.
"And there is no escape!" her father cried.
"You are marched off at dawn to work in the fields.
An overseer stands guard with his whip.
If you do manage to run away
and hide in the woods,
you are hunted down. No escape!"

Hattie shivered.
She wished her father would stop,
but she knew he would go on
until he had convinced everyone that slavery was a sin
that *must not* exist in America,
the land of the free.
He would go on and on until
half the congregation was crying.
Hattie could hardly breathe.

At last the service was over.
Hattie ran out into the sunshine, catching her breath.
Catherine came up beside her. "Oh, Kate," Hattie said,
"thank heaven we do not have slavery in Connecticut."
Catherine nodded. "It is an evil that must be ended
everywhere someday.
Now tell me. Are you packed?"

"Packed?" said Hattie.
"Harriet!" said Catherine sharply.
"The stagecoach for Hartford leaves early tomorrow.
I hope you will be ready."

Hattie was jolted back to her own life.
She was leaving home to study
in the new school for girls
that Catherine had started in Hartford.

"You can do some teaching too," Catherine had said
when the plans were made.
"Teaching? Me?" Hattie stared at her sister.
"You're thirteen," Catherine said.
"You know enough Latin to teach beginners.
Besides, be sensible.

You may need to earn your living someday.
What else can a woman do but teach?
You should be preparing yourself."
Hattie knew there was no use arguing.
Now, outside the church, she said,
"I'll be ready, Kate."
Early next morning, her little trunk
was lifted onto the stagecoach.
She sat beside Catherine.
They were on their way.

When school began, Hattie got up at dawn
to study the lesson she must teach
to other girls later on.
When she stood in the classroom,
all her students seemed bigger than she.
Her voice was a whisper.
"Please open your books to the first chapter."

Somehow, she got through the hour.
Then she had her own classes to go to.
The day seemed endless.
So did the next day. And the next.

All Hattie did was study, teach,
and then creep into bed at night.

Finally she began to find the work easier.
She even had a little extra time
to start writing a play.
One day she was enjoying herself,
imagining and writing,
when Catherine came to her room.
"Well," said Catherine, "if you have this much free time,
you can teach another class."

Hattie put away the play.
She did not think of herself as a slave.
No iron bracelets clanked on her wrists.
She was finding friends among the girls,
and sometimes they went walking together,
and talked and laughed.
But she did know how it felt
to get up at dawn
and to work all day
with someone always watching to make sure
she did not idle—or escape.

4

Bump, crash, clump!
The wagon bumped over the logs
laid crosswise in the mud
to make the "corduroy road."
Hattie held tightly to the wagon seat,
squeezed in with Catherine and George and Charley.
Across from them
sat their father and stepmother,
and little half sister, Isabella,
and half brothers, Thomas and Jamey.

But no matter how tightly they all held on,
they were jolted and bumped and jolted again
as they traveled over the corduroy roads
of Pennsylvania and Ohio.
Lyman Beecher had decided to leave New England
to become the head of a new college for ministers
in the Far West—Cincinnati, Ohio.
Catherine was going along
to start a new school for girls.
All the family were going, except the older boys,
who were still in school in the East.

Bump, crash, clump!
Lyman Beecher laughed.
"It's one sure cure for stomachaches," he said.
"Let's sing another hymn."
They all joined in:

On Jordon's stormy banks I stand,
and cast a wishful eye
To Canaan's promised land . . .

A farmer rounding up his cows stared in surprise
at the wagonload of singing strangers.

George waved at him,
and on they went, singing, joking,
trying to laugh even when something went wrong,
like the wagon getting stuck deep in mud.

For Hattie, it was all an adventure.
She was leaving the dreary work
of the Hartford school behind.
A new life was beginning.
She had no idea what it would be like,
but at least it would be different.
At last she saw a jumble of rooftops and steeples
rising beside the wide Ohio River,
and a jumble of steamboats lining the riverfront.
They rode into the city, past warehouses
surrounded by bales of cotton and pens filled with pigs.
"So many pigs!" said Harriet, staring.
"That's right," said George.
"Cincinnati ships so much bacon and ham
that its nickname is Porkopolis."

But beyond the warehouses and business buildings,
the hills looked green and friendly.

The college was up in the hills
and the Beechers found a home there.
Lyman Beecher began his work at the college.
Catherine hurried to rent rooms for her school
and Hattie trailed around after her,
taking in everything.
So many brick buildings
instead of wooden ones like back home.
Such a fine market in the center of the city.
Such crowds of people, black as well as white.
She took it for granted that the black people,
busy at various jobs, were free.
What she couldn't admire—
like pigs let loose in the streets to eat the garbage—
she decided was funny.

But then—

$100 REWARD!

FOR CAPTURE OF RUNAWAY SLAVE!

When Hattie saw the sign
posted on the side of a building, she stopped short.

All her life, her father had preached
against the sin of slavery,
but slavery had been far away.
Now it was very close.

She looked from the sign toward the river.
Across that broad river was Kentucky,
where slavery was legal.
Across that river,
black men, women, and children were *owned*
by white people.
If any of them tried to run away,
their owners advertised for them, as though
they were dogs or horses.

A black woman walked by,
carrying a basket of groceries.
Hattie saw her look back over her shoulder.
Was she really free? Hattie wondered.
Or did she fear someone was following her?
A black man sat in a jitney cab at the corner,
waiting for a passenger.
Was he really a free man
or a runaway slave?

30

Hattie looked back at the sign —

$100 REWARD!

Suddenly the city seemed like a dangerous forest.
She imagined black people darting and hiding
and trembling at every sound.

"Are runaways often captured?"
Hattie asked her father that evening.
"Caught and sent back and —"
She stopped. "*Why* would anyone want to capture
another human being who is only trying to be *free*?"

Lyman Beecher sighed.
"Here in Cincinnati, men buy and sell cotton
grown by slave labor down South.
They want to stay friendly with the cotton growers.
So they return Southern property whenever they can."

"A human life!" Hattie cried. "A human soul — property!"
Lyman Beecher shook his head helplessly.
He was learning that people in Cincinnati
grew angry if he spoke out against the system
that made money for them.
"It's going to take time," he said. "Time."

Hattie stared at her father
with a hollow feeling inside.

She did the things she had to do.
She taught in Catherine's school.
At home she helped with
the sewing and other chores.
She joined a literary club
and began to write again.
Far away from New England,
she was remembering and writing
about things back home, the things she loved.
When her first story was published in a magazine
and won a prize,
she was happier than she let anyone know.

But every day she saw the advertisements:

$50 REWARD FOR ANY INFORMATION
ABOUT RUNAWAY SLAVE
$100 REWARD FOR CAPTURE OF SLAVE NANCY

And down by the waterfront,
she saw the steamboats carrying slaves from Kentucky,
to be sold in the Deep South.

She stared at the men and women
chained together on the lower decks.
One day she saw a young black woman holding a baby.
As she watched, a white man came up to the woman,
spoke a moment, then grabbed the baby
and hurried away.

Had he sold the mother away from her child?
Had he sold the baby to someone else?
Hattie had no way of knowing.
But she saw the woman's face
and her outstretched arms.

Hattie could not forget that mother's face.
Sometimes she saw it in her dreams
and woke up as from a nightmare.

5

It was evening.
Harriet and her father and a young professor
named Calvin Stowe
sat on the porch of a house
high on the riverbank
a little way from Cincinnati.
They were visiting the Reverend John Rankin.
Their voices were quiet as darkness fell
over the river and the far Kentucky shore.
"Excuse me a moment," said the Reverend Rankin.

He went into the house, lit a lamp,
and placed it carefully in a window.
When the minister returned, Lyman Beecher laughed.
"We hardly need the light, Rankin.
There will soon be a moon."
The Reverend Rankin looked at them a moment.
"I know you are all against slavery," he said.
Lyman Beecher looked surprised. "Of course."
Harriet nodded and Calvin Stowe did too.
"Of course."

The minister said, "I did not light the lamp for us.
That lamp in my window can be seen
across the river in Kentucky.
Any slaves there who see that light
know I will give them food and shelter
and help them get to someone farther North
who will help them travel farther still,
until at last they are safe in Canada."

Lyman Beecher whistled softly.
"The Underground Railway," Hattie breathed.
"You are part of it."

The minister nodded. "A very small part."

Calvin Stowe spoke quietly.
"Have many runaways come across the river?"
"Yes," said the Reverend Rankin, "quite a few."
"Please," said Harriet, "tell us about some of them."

The minister saw her leaning foward
and heard the eagerness in her voice.
"I will always remember one young woman," he said.
"It was late winter. The river was still frozen,
but the ice was beginning to thaw
and break up in great chunks. A dangerous time.
Still, over in Kentucky, a young mother
was desperate to escape from her owner.
Carrying her child in her arms,
she stepped out onto the soft ice.
Then she ran and jumped from
one floating sheet of ice to another until, finally,
she made it to the Ohio shore.
Just as she was safe on the land,
the ice broke with a roar,
and went rushing and crashing down the river.

If she and her child had crossed five minutes later,
they would have drowned."
Harriet's eyes closed.
"A miracle," she whispered.
The Reverend Rankin told of other runaways.
Harriet listened to each story
as if *she* were the one running for her life.
But the story of that young mother crossing the ice
stirred her the most.

Later, she and Calvin Stowe
walked along the edge of the bluff.
They talked about the risks
the Reverend Rankin was taking.
There were men in his congregation
who would try to ruin him
if they learned what he was doing.

Harriet told Calvin
about a visit she had made recently
to a plantation in Kentucky.
"I have to admit," she said slowly,
"the Negroes—the slaves—
seemed content and well treated."
Calvin said, "That is the side of slavery
Southerners prefer to talk about.
They say they are like parents to their slaves."

Harriet nodded. "I saw it. Not all
slave owners are monsters."
"Perhaps," said Calvin, "it would be wise for
anti-slavery speakers and writers to admit that."
"Yes," said Harriet.

40

"That might make the evil of slavery even *plainer.*
Even the kindest master may find he has to sell
some of his property."

Calvin agreed. "There is the evil.
People are not property."

They talked until the moon was almost down,
getting to know each other,
and seeing that they felt the same way
about many things.

6

"Ma-ma, Ma-ma!" the twins sang,
beating on the table with their spoons.
In his high chair, baby Henry laughed
and began to beat with his spoon too.
"All right," Harriet called,
hurrying into the kitchen with a pitcher of milk.
"Here is bedtime milk for all of you."
She smiled at the pretty twins, Hattie and Eliza,
and baby Henry.
It was five years since she had married
the young professor, Calvin Stowe.

The twins were four years old and Henry two.
Harriet had cares and worries
she had never known before.
But she loved her husband and babies
and only wished that Calvin made more money
teaching at the college.
Tonight, again, after the children were in bed,
she would stay awake and write.
She had found she could sell short stories and articles
to magazines and religious papers.
She was not paid much but every dollar helped.

"Hold out your mug, Eliza," Harriet was saying,
when she heard a knock at the door.
"Just a moment," she said and went to open the door.

A young black woman
who helped Harriet with the housework
was standing outside in the dark.
"Why, Zillah," said Harriet. "Come in."
"Oh yes, Mrs. Stowe, yes," Zillah whispered.
She came in quickly and pushed the door shut.
"What on earth is wrong, Zillah?" asked Harriet.

"My old master's here in the city."
Zillah was still whispering.
Her eyes were wide and frightened.
"I think he saw me downtown."

"Your old master?" asked Harriet.
"But you're free, aren't you? You told me you were."
"Oh, Mrs. Stowe, I thought it was safe to say so.
I never thought the master would come way up
from Tennessee.
But he's here.
I'm sure he saw me.
Oh, I have to get away."

Harriet's hand went out to Zillah's.
"Don't be frightened," she said quickly.
"We will help you."
She turned to the children.
"Be good for a few minutes while Mama is busy."
She took Zillah's arm.
"You can hide in the cellar for now.
When Mr. Stowe gets home,
we will figure out what to do next."

44

When Zillah was hidden,
Harriet put the children to bed,
but her thoughts were racing, figuring out plans.

Calvin came home
and wanted to help, of course.
But he was a worrying man
and kept thinking of things that could go wrong.
At last Harriet went down the road to her brother
Henry Ward. "We must get Zillah away
from the city," she said.
Henry Ward said, "I know a farmer
out on the northern road.
He's part of the Underground.
I'll get a wagon and be at your house in half an hour."

Home again, Harriet found a dark dress and bonnet
and hurried down to the cellar.
"It will be all right," she said
as she helped Zillah change.
At last she heard Calvin call softly
from the top of the stairs.
"Henry's here."

Harriet hurried Zillah out into the night.
She helped her hide in the back of the wagon.
Calvin got up on the seat beside Henry.
Henry flicked the reins and they were off.

After that, Harriet sat in the kitchen.
She couldn't write. She couldn't do anything
except wait and hope and listen —
for the *clip-clop* of a horse
stopping in front of the house,
the sound of footsteps on the porch.

The minutes ticked away on the big old clock,
tick-tock-tick.
The house made the creaking sounds it always
made at night. The hours passed.

Early in the morning, Calvin and Henry returned.
Zillah was safe with the farmer.
He had promised to hide her until the next night,
when he would send her to the next person
on the Underground Railway.
Harriet sighed with relief.

"Yes," said Calvin. "At last we've helped *somebody*."
Harriet rubbed her eyes and shook her head.
"But Calvin," she said,
"there are so many, many others—"

Suddenly Harriet felt she had been living
close to the miseries of slavery forever.
All she wanted was to run away herself,
to run far, far away
from the sights and sounds of suffering.

7

"Is it really true?"
Harriet could hardly believe it.
Bowdoin College, in Maine, was asking Calvin Stowe
to come and be a professor there.
The salary offered was very low.
"But you'll accept, won't you?" Harriet pleaded.
Calvin nodded.

Harriet hurried around the Cincinnati house
getting ready for the great move.

She had five children now,
another boy, Fred, and a little girl, Georgiana.
But packing for all of them
seemed no trouble to Harriet.
She was escaping at last
from a city that had never seemed like home.
Most of all, she was going far away from slavery.

They traveled by steamboat,
changed to railway cars, then to a canalboat,
then back to railway cars again.

They were getting on the cars in New Jersey
when Calvin bought a newspaper
and read the latest news.
He looked upset as he hurried to Harriet.
"Congress is passing a new law," he said.
"From now on it will be a *federal crime*
to help a runaway slave."

"What?" gasped Harriet. Calvin went on,
"There's more. Special agents will be hired
to hunt down black people
suspected of being runaways."

Harriet reached for the newspaper.
As she read the story, she seemed to hear
heavy footsteps coming closer and closer to *her*,
a door broken down, chains clanking,
and then one of *her* children torn from her arms.
"Oh, no, no," she whispered.
But no one was hunting down Harriet and her family.

They traveled on to Brooklyn
where her brother Henry Ward was
the minister of a large church.
All he wanted to talk about
was this new law, the Fugitive Slave Act.
"I'm preaching about it this Sunday," he told Harriet.
"I'm saying—" He paused.
"I am saying it is a bad law which should be disobeyed.
There is a higher law, God's law,
which demands that all people be free."

Harriet's eyes shone as she looked at her brother.
"Yes," she said,
"it is a terrible thing to say a law is wrong,
but this one is."

The Stowes went on to Boston
where Harriet's brother Edward was a minister.
Edward also was preaching that the new law
should be disobeyed.
One afternoon,
while the children were busy with their books,
Harriet talked to her brother's wife.
"Both Edward and Henry are doing so much," she said.
"If only there were something *I* could do."

"There is," said her sister-in-law.
"You can write."
Harriet said, "But all I have written are simple stories
to earn a little money."

Edward's wife insisted.
"If I could use a pen as you can,
I'd write something to make people *feel*
what a dreadful thing slavery is."

Harriet stared at her.
Suddenly she stood up.
Young Hattie, Eliza, Henry, and Freddie looked up at her.

All their lives they would remember
what their mother said then,
and the way she said it,
like a vow.
"I will write something. I *will!*"

8

But she had so much else to do.
She and her family had to travel on to Maine.
She had to find a house, and furnish it.
Soon after they were settled,
Harriet's last child was born.
Little Charles was a healthy baby.
The older children, Hattie and Eliza, Henry,
Fred, and Georgiana, played in the brisk Maine air
or explored along the waterfront,
where sailing ships were built.

Calvin began his new work.
Everything in Harriet's world was peaceful.

But day after day, letters and newspapers
brought the news.
Black men, women, and children
who had run away from slavery
were being hunted and caught and sent back South.
The dreadful manhunt was under way.

"I will write something," Harriet had said.
So she went about her tasks,
but part of her mind was busy
trying to think of a story
that would make people *feel* the evil of slavery.

But no story came.

In Brooklyn, her brother Henry Ward
was preaching fiery sermons against the new law.
In Boston, brother Edward was preaching and writing.

And what was Harriet doing?
Nothing.

One Sunday, when Calvin was away,
Harriet sat in church,
the twins and the baby on one side,
Henry and Fred and Georgiana on the other.
The sermon was going on as usual,
when Harriet suddenly stopped paying attention.
She was seeing a picture in her mind.

A black man was being beaten by two cruel men
while another man, a white man,
urged them on.

Who were these people?
Why were they beating the black man?
Harriet was not sure.
It seemed to her that the black man
was trying to protect someone who had run away.
The others were trying to make him tell
where the runaway had gone.
But Uncle Tom would not tell.

Uncle Tom?
Where had that name come from?
Harriet did not know.

She just knew that Uncle Tom
was the name of the black man
who was being beaten so cruelly.

There was a burst of singing around her.
Everyone was standing up.
Harriet realized she was still in church
and the service was ending with a hymn.

In a dream, she walked home with the children.
Then she sat down and started writing out
the picture she had seen.
Her pen raced along.
She hardly heard the baby crying
or Freddie and Georgiana asking
when dinner would be ready.

When she had finished,
she called the children.
"Listen," she said and began to read
the scene she had written.
Hattie and Eliza were crying before she had finished.
"Oh, Mama," Henry said,
"slavery is the cruelest thing in the world."

Harriet nodded.
She folded up the writing, put it in a drawer,
and got dinner.
After that, she almost forgot it.
Calvin came home
and she never thought to tell him about it.

One day Calvin found the scribbled notes.
He read them.
Then he went to her and took her hands.
Harriet saw tears in his eyes.
"That's it, Hattie," he said.
"That's the start of what you want to write.
You must go on."

Harriet said, "But there is so much I don't know:
where the story starts, how Uncle Tom got there,
why the men are beating him—"

Calvin said, "It will come to you.
You just have to go on."

9

She wrote at the kitchen table
while dinner was cooking and pies were baking.
She wrote on the back steps
while the children were washing up.
She wrote in the parlor on a rickety table
while Calvin wrote his lectures at the desk.
She wrote and wrote,
for the story *had* begun to come to her.
She started it on a pleasant plantation in Kentucky,
like the one she had visited near Cincinnati.

She made Uncle Tom a trusted slave there.
But suddenly his master needed money.
He had to sell some of his slaves.

He decided to sell Uncle Tom
and a clever little boy who was the son
of a beautiful young woman named Eliza.
Eliza could not bear to lose her son.
She ran away with him one dark winter night.

Now Harriet remembered the true story
the Reverend Rankin had told her long ago
in Cincinnati.
She had her Eliza come to the half-frozen river.
She had her Eliza pick up her child
and then leap out onto the ice,
just as that other runaway had done.
She wrote of Eliza jumping from one ice sheet to another,
escaping the slave hunters.
Harriet's pen rushed along
trying to keep up with Eliza's flight.
But Uncle Tom was another sort of person.
He would not run away.

He tried to accept what happened as God's will,
and to be strong enough to bear it without complaining.
So he was sold and sent down the river
to New Orleans.

Now the terrible sights
of the Cincinnati waterfront
crowded into Harriet's mind as she had Uncle Tom
driven aboard a steamboat.
She wrote of the mother she had seen
whose baby was snatched from her.
She filled page after page with scenes she remembered.
But then, in New Orleans, Uncle Tom
was bought by a kind man.
Harriet wanted to show that *some* slave owners
were decent people,
and for a while Uncle Tom was almost happy.

But then . . . then . . .

Harriet could hardly keep up with the story
as it unfolded itself in her mind.
She wrote and wrote,
never stopping to change anything.

64

Every so often, she bundled up some pages
and sent them to the editor of a magazine
in Washington, D.C.
Parts of the story were printed
week after week.
Soon the editor began to get letters.
"Thank you for the wonderful new story,"
wrote one reader.
"I have never read anything like it," wrote another.
"For the first time, I begin to *feel*
the evil of slavery," wrote still another.

A man who published books read some of the story.
He wrote to Harriet that he wanted
to publish it as a book.

Finally, Harriet was writing of Uncle Tom's death
after the cruel beating.
There were tears in her eyes,
but she knew it had to be.
Uncle Tom would never betray a fellow man
even if it cost him his life.
And she wrote that he too had escaped from slavery
into the freedom of heaven.

The long, long story had come to an end.
Harriet could hardly believe it.
She had lived so long with Uncle Tom,
Eliza, and all the others.

She stood in the little post office
and handed the last bundle of pages to the postmaster.
Suddenly *she* felt free—wonderfully free.
It was as though she too had run away
from everything that had hurt her
as she followed all the slaves in her story
to freedom.

At home, she called the children
to get ready for a picnic on the shore.
"We'll slice some of the ham
and take some boiled potatoes.
We'll have a lovely day!"

10

"UNCLE TOM'S CABIN? I'm sorry, madam,
we're all sold out," the man in the bookstore said.
"But the book was just published," said the woman.
The bookseller said, "I know. I know.
I hope more copies will arrive soon.
Everybody's asking for that new book
by Harriet Beecher Stowe."
Ten thousand copies, thirty thousand copies,
fifty thousand— people were buying the book
as fast as it was delivered.
Everybody was talking about it.

UNCLE TOM'S CABIN.
That was a curious title.
Harriet's story had little to do with any cabin.
It was mostly about the different ways
black people ran away to freedom.
Running away—
through all sorts of dangers—
to places where they could call their lives their own.

Suddenly the book was exciting people in England too.
Then people were reading it in France,
in Germany, in Sweden, in Russia,
in every country of Europe,
and soon in Asia too.

The story made people cry. It made them laugh.
It made them *care*.

Harriet's first check from the publisher
was for ten thousand dollars.
She and Calvin stared at it
and then looked at each other.
Life would be much easier now.

Then came bad news.
Almost everybody in America
might be reading the book,
but not everybody was *liking* it.
Down South, in the slave states,
readers were realizing this book was *dangerous*.
It made people feel *too* strongly.

Critics wrote in Southern papers
that the book was full of lies,
the work of a crazy Northern woman
who knew nothing about slavery.

Many Southern states
refused to allow the book to cross their borders.
Booksellers could go to jail if they sold copies.
Harriet began to get letters from Southerners,
cursing her and threatening her.

Harriet was horrified and bewildered.
"But I based everything
on what I'd heard or seen myself,
on things I *know* happened."

Meantime, nothing could stop her book.
Thousands of people,
millions of people,
who had never heard
Lyman Beecher speak against slavery,
who had never heard Harriet's brothers
nor any of the anti-slavery preachers
who spoke up and down the land—
these millions were reading Harriet's words.

11

The quarrel between the North and South over slavery
was like a storm coming closer and closer.

Harriet wrote another book about slavery.
She wrote a novel about New England.
She wrote stories and articles for magazines.
She was famous.
People wanted to read everything she wrote.
Then a tall, homely man from Illinois
was elected President of the United States.
His name was Abraham Lincoln.

He was against slavery.
The people of the South vowed to leave the Union
if he took office.

He took office
and the Southern states did leave the Union.
In April 1861,
the Civil War began.

A year a half later,
with her youngest son, Charley, beside her,
Harriet walked into a sitting room
in the White House in Washington, D.C.
A tall, thin man came forward.
He looked down at her as he held out his hand.
"So this is the little lady
who started this great big war,"
said Abraham Lincoln to Harriet Beecher Stowe.

Harriet shook her head.
Many things had led to the terrible war.
But she knew that her book had done a great deal
to make thousands of Northerners
ready to fight for the end of slavery.

So she felt she had a certain right
to visit the President of the United States
and ask him why he had not freed the slaves
even though the armies had been fighting
for almost two years.

Lincoln said he understood her concern.
But "The Union must come first," he said.
"And now that our Union troops
are winning some battles at last,
I can promise that you will soon hear news
that will make you happy."

Harriet felt content.
"He is a great man," she said to Charley later.
"He will keep his word."

And he did.
On January 1, 1863, Abraham Lincoln issued
the Emancipation Proclamation
declaring that all slaves in the states
at war with the Union were free.
When the news was announced,
Harriet was in a large theater in Philadelphia.

74

Everyone cheered and shouted and sang.
Then someone saw Harriet in the balcony.
"Mrs. Stowe!" someone cried.
"There she is! Up there!" called someone else.
"Mrs. Stowe! Mrs. Stowe!"

Everyone began to wave or flutter handerchiefs,
to smile and blow kisses.
They knew how much she had done
to make people feel the wrong of slavery.
And they were thanking her.

12

Harriet wrote many more books.
All of them were popular.
She made enough money
to help many men and women who had once been slaves,
and to make a good life for herself and her family.
But never again did she write a book
like UNCLE TOM'S CABIN.
On her seventieth birthday,
at a large garden party in her honor,
the poet Oliver Wendell Holmes read a poem
he had written for her.

He compared her most famous book to a lever
which a small woman had lifted
to change a world.
(Did Harriet remember supper table debates, long ago,
when she had called the lever
man's most useful invention?)

For some secret reason,
Harriet knew what it was like
to feel trapped
and not able to call her life her own.
She knew the need to run away.
And so she was able to write a book
that made people feel
what it was like to be a slave,
wanting just one thing—
freedom.

Her lever was the wand of art,
Her fulcrum was the human heart,
    Whence all unfailing aid is.
She moved the earth! . . .

OLIVER WENDELL HOLMES

Author's Note

Harriet Beecher Stowe was born on June 14, 1811, in Litchfield, Connecticut. She was the sixth of the eight children of Lyman and Roxanna Beecher. Her mother died when she was five, and a year later her father married again. In due time there were three more children in the Beecher family.

In the early nineteenth century, when Harriet was growing up, women had few choices in life except to get married, keep house, and raise a family. If a woman did not get married (as Harriet's sister Catherine did not), she might teach school, but usually she only taught girls. Women were not considered capable of teaching boys older than six or seven. (In her later years, Catherine Beecher spent a lot of time and energy trying to change people's minds about this.) A woman might also be a dressmaker or work at some menial job in one of the textile mills that were springing up all over the country. But that was it. A woman couldn't hope to be a minister, a doctor, a lawyer, a banker, or a scientist.

There were no colleges for women when Harriet was young— no schools for girls that offered courses like those men studied. Women's brains were not supposed to be strong enough for such studies. And of course women could not vote.

Since women suffered so many restrictions, it is not surprising that they were especially sympathetic to the plight of black slaves. Women helped to organize the first anti-slavery societies in the North. In fact, they banded together to help fight slavery before they began to organize to win the right to vote and other rights for themselves. Working in the anti-slavery movements, a few daring souls even broke the taboo against women speaking in public to lecture on the evils of slavery.

The Fugitive Slave Act was passed in 1850. Congress dreamed it up as a reward for Southern slave owners, who let California enter the union as a free state where slavery was not allowed. It was part of a "compromise" between pro-slavery and anti-slavery people, designed to keep the union together. It did not work for long.

Harriet died in Hartford, Connecticut, in 1896, after a life that had very nearly spanned the century.